volume 9

COLOR / TEÑIDO / COULEUR

138 hairstyles

138 peinados

138 coiffures

HAIR'S HOW ®

Content / Contenido / Contenu

Cover: **Hair**_Ameila LaRosa for Heading Out Hair & Beauty **Make-up**_Aleesa Hall **Style**_Emma Cotterill **Photo**_Andrew O'Toole

Hair's How
Blond/Rubio/Blond

Hairstyle/Peinado/Coiffure_Llongueras Team
Style/Estilo/Style_Lluis Llongueras
Photo/Foto/Photo_Oleg Covian

Hairstyle/Peinado/Coiffure_Suzie McGill for Rainbow Room International
Make-up/Maquillaje/Maquillage_Lee Pearson
Style/Estilo/Style_Bernard Connolly
Photo/Foto/Photo_Christophe Cohen

Hairstyle/Peinado/Coiffure_Mark Leeson, Mark Leeson Hair, Body & Mind
Make-up/Maquillaje/Maquillage_Aleesa Hall
Style/Estilo/Style_Bernard Connolly
Photo/Foto/Photo_Andrew O'Toole

Hairstyle/Peinado/Coiffure_Jean Claude Aubry International
Photo/Foto/Photo_Laurent Darmon

Hairstyle/Peinado/Coiffure_Andrew Barton, Alison Dace, Tracey Gallagher for Saks
Make-up/Maquillaje/Maquillage_Carol Brown
Photo/Foto/Photo_Darren Feist

Hairstyle/Peinado/Coiffure_Sonia Lyon for Toni&Guy
Make-up/Maquillaje/Maquillage_Kellie Ritchie
Style/Estilo/Style_Emma Cotterill
Photo/Foto/Photo_Andrew O'Toole

Hairstyle/Peinado/Coiffure_Heading Out Hair & Beauty

Hairstyle/Peinado/Coiffure_Heading Out Hair & Beauty

Hairstyle/Peinado/Coiffure_Intercoiffure France Team
Make-up/Maquillaje/Maquillage_Sebastian
Style/Estilo/Style_Gaélle Bon
Photo/Foto/Photo_Yannick Touzan

Hairstyle/Peinado/Coiffure_Dessange
Photo/Foto/Photo_Nathalie Demontes

Hairstyle/Peinado/Coiffure_Paul Gehring
Make-up/Maquillaje/Maquillage_Christina Marzo, Fabrizio Camponeschi
Photo/Foto/Photo_Carlo Battillocchi

Hairstyle/Peinado/Coiffure_B salon creative team
Make-up/Maquillaje/Maquillage_Pascal Tesser @ B creatives
Style/Estilo/Style_Miquel Mohamedjar @ B creatives
Photo/Foto/Photo_Jan Andraschko

Hairstyle/Peinado/Coiffure_Jean-Luc Amarin for Camille Albane
Photo/Foto/Photo_Nathalie Demontes

Hairstyle/Peinado/Coiffure_Trevor Sorbie Team
Make-up/Maquillaje/Maquillage_Makky
Photo/Foto/Photo_Trevor Leighton

Hairstyle/Peinado/Coiffure_Trevor Sorbie Team
Make-up/Maquillaje/Maquillage_Makky
Photo/Foto/Photo_Trevor Leighton

Hairstyle/Peinado/Coiffure_William Lepec and Saint Karl Team
Make-up/Maquillaje/Maquillage_Vesna Estord
Style/Estilo/Style_Kathrin Lezinsky
Photo/Foto/Photo_JF Verganti

Hairstyle/Peinado/Coiffure_William Lepec and Saint Karl Team
Make-up/Maquillaje/Maquillage_Vesna Estord
Style/Estilo/Style_Kathrin Lezinsky
Photo/Foto/Photo_JF Verganti

Hairstyle/Peinado/Coiffure_William Lepec and Saint Karl Team
Make-up/Maquillaje/Maquillage_Vesna Estord
Style/Estilo/Style_Kathrin Lezinsky
Photo/Foto/Photo_JF Verganti

Hairstyle/Peinado/Coiffure_Beverly Rosser
& Beth Sawyer @ Bobbers Hairdressing

Hairstyle/Peinado/Coiffure_Coiff1rst Team
Photo/Foto/Photo_Eric Pfalzgraf

Hairstyle/Peinado/Coiffure_Ben White & The Eleven Hair Art Team
Coloring/Teñido/Coloration_Jason Welch **Make-up/Maquillaje/Maquillage_***Hannah Wynne*
Style/Estilo/Style_Hannah Wynne **Photo/Foto/Photo_***Kyoko Homma*

Hairstyle/Peinado/Coiffure_Luke Walton @ Rainbow Room International
Make-up/Maquillaje/Maquillage_Lee Pearson
Style/Estilo/Style_Bernard Connolly Photo/Foto/Photo_Christopher Cohen

Hairstyle/Peinado/Coiffure_Luke Walton @ Rainbow Room International
Make-up/Maquillaje/Maquillage_Lee Pearson
Style/Estilo/Style_Bernard Connolly
Photo/Foto/Photo_Christopher Cohen

Hairstyle/Peinado/Coiffure_Luke Walton @ Rainbow Room International
Make-up/Maquillaje/Maquillage_Lee Pearson
Style/Estilo/Style_Bernard Connolly
Photo/Foto/Photo_Christopher Cohen

Hairstyle/Peinado/Coiffure_Paterson SA Team
Make-up/Maquillaje/Maquillage_Rhona Stewart
Style/Estilo/Style_Bernard Connolly **Photo/Foto/Photo_Jonathon West**

Hairstyle/Peinado/Coiffure_Paterson SA Team
Make-up/Maquillaje/Maquillage_Rhona Stewart
Style/Estilo/Style_Bernard Connolly
Photo/Foto/Photo_Jonathon West

Hairstyle/Peinado/Coiffure_Pavel Vaan
Make-up/Maquillaje/Maquillage_Pavel Vaan
Photo/Foto/Photo_studio «Koma»

Hairstyle/Peinado/Coiffure_Felix Fischer, Darren Ambrose
for Wella Professionals
Photo/Foto/Photo_Sarah Silver

Hairstyle/Peinado/Coiffure_Eugenia Dubchak, beauty salon «Dolores»

Hairstyle/Peinado/Coiffure_Jean Claude Biguine

Hairstyle/Peinado/Coiffure_Jean-Marc Maniatis for Any d'Avray

Hairstyle/Peinado/Coiffure_Jean-Marie Contreras

Hairstyle/Peinado/Coiffure_Dmitry Vinokurov

Hairstyle/Peinado/Coiffure_Jean-Marc Maniatis for Any d'Avray

Hairstyle/Peinado/Coiffure_Luke Walton @ Rainbow Room International
Make-up/Maquillaje/Maquillage_Lee Pearson
Style/Estilo/Style_Bernard Connolly
Photo/Foto/Photo_Christopher Cohen

Hairstyle/Peinado/Coiffure_Raffel Pages Team
Make-up/Maquillaje/Maquillage_Raffel Pages Team
Photo/Foto/Photo_S. Jasanada

Hairstyle/Peinado/Coiffure_Colin Greaney for Mahogany
Coloring/Teñido/Coloration_Ciara Fagan & Vivica Davies
Style/Estilo/Style_Amy Abrahams

Hairstyle/Peinado/Coiffure_Klaus Peter Ochs

Hairstyle/Peinado/Coiffure_The Cutting Room Team
Style/Estilo/Style_Darren Knight
Photo/Foto/Photo_Rick Dodds

Hairstyle/Peinado/Coiffure_Cathy Monnier and Saint Algue Team   Hairstyle/Peinado/Coiffure_Dessange
Make-up/Maquillaje/Maquillage_Luc Droguen
Style/Estilo/Style_Alexandra Tesson
Photo/Foto/Photo_Gilles-Marie Zimmermann

Hairstyle/Peinado/Coiffure_Bundy Bundy Team
Style/Estilo/Style_Bundy Bundy Team
Photo/Foto/Photo_Inge Prader

Hairstyle/Peinado/Coiffure_Gandini International Team
Make-up/Maquillaje/Maquillage_Stefania Pellizzaro
Style/Estilo/Style_Silvia Cicchetti
Photo/Foto/Photo_Paulo Renftle

Hairstyle/Peinado/Coiffure_Glenn van Dijke and Keune Studio Team for Keune Haircosmetics
Make-up/Maquillaje/Maquillage_Dominique Samuelsen
Style/Estilo/Style_Pedro Dias
Photo/Foto/Photo_Hans de Vries

Hairstyle/Peinado/Coiffure_Kai Uwe Steeg

*Hairstyle/Peinado/Coiffure*_Mark Leeson Artistic Team, Mark Leeson Hair, Body & Mind
*Make-up/Maquillaje/Maquillage*_Kylie O'Toole
*Style/Estilo/Style*_Emma Cotterill
*Photo/Foto/Photo*_Andrew O'Toole

Hairstyle/Peinado/Coiffure_Jean Claude Aubry International
Photo/Foto/Photo_Laurent Darmon

Hairstyle/Peinado/Coiffure_Gandini International Team
Make-up/Maquillaje/Maquillage_Stefania Pellizzaro
Style/Estilo/Style_Silvia Cicchetti
Photo/Foto/Photo_Paulo Renftle

Dark/Oscuro/Brun

Hairstyle/Peinado/Coiffure_Jean Claude Biguine

Hairstyle/Peinado/Coiffure_Heading Out Hair & Beauty

Hairstyle/Peinado/Coiffure_Sharon Cox for Sanrizz
Make-up/Maquillaje/Maquillage_Lee Pearson
Style/Estilo/Style_Rachel Bakewell Photo/Foto/Photo_Andres Reynaga

Hairstyle/Peinado/Coiffure_Terry Calvert for Clipso
Make-up/Maquillaje/Maquillage_Janet Francis
Style/Estilo/Style_Harriet Cotterill Photo/Foto/Photo_Martin Evening

47

Hairstyle/Peinado/Coiffure_Harry Boocock for Hair Studio
Make-up/Maquillaje/Maquillage_Janet Francis
Style/Estilo/Style_Peter Breen
Photo/Foto/Photo_Jim Crone

Hairstyle/Peinado/Coiffure_Philippe Tapprest for René Furterer

Hairstyle/Peinado/Coiffure_Colin Greaney for Mahogany
Coloring/Teñido/Coloration_Ciara Fagan & Vivica Davies
Style/Estilo/Style_Amy Abrahams

Hairstyle/Peinado/Coiffure_Franck Pérez, Jean Louis David

Hairstyle/Peinado/Coiffure_Cathy Monnier and Saint Algue Team
Make-up/Maquillaje/Maquillage_Luc Droguen
Style/Estilo/Style_Alexandra Tesson
Photo/Foto/Photo_Gilles-Marie Zimmermann

Hairstyle/Peinado/Coiffure_Alexandre Zouari
Make-up/Maquillaje/Maquillage_Corinne Le Breton
Style/Estilo/Style_Karine Martins
Photo/Foto/Photo_Sandra Fourqui

Hairstyle/Peinado/Coiffure_Sanrizz Team

Hairstyle/Peinado/Coiffure_Dessange
Photo/Foto/Photo_Nathalie Demontes

Hairstyle/Peinado/Coiffure_Dessange
Photo/Foto/Photo_Nathalie Demontes

Hairstyle/Peinado/Coiffure_B salon creative team
Make-up/Maquillaje/Maquillage_Pascal Tesser @ B creatives
Style/Estilo/Style_Miquel Mohamedjar @ B creatives
Photo/Foto/Photo_Jan Andraschko

Hairstyle/Peinado/Coiffure_Goldwell Creative Team

Hairstyle/Peinado/Coiffure_Goldwell Creative Team

Hairstyle/Peinado/Coiffure_Jean-Marie Contreras   *Hairstyle/Peinado/Coiffure_Jean-Marie Contreras*

Hairstyle/Peinado/Coiffure_Italian Style Framesi
Make-up/Maquillaje/Maquillage_S. Dell'Orto
Style/Estilo/Style_D. Eugeni, A. Argentieri
Products/Productos/Produits_Framesi

Hairstyle/Peinado/Coiffure_William Lepec and Intermède Team
Make-up/Maquillaje/Maquillage_Vesna Estord
Style/Estilo/Style_Kathrin Lezinsk
Photo/Foto/Photo_Saima Altunkaya

Hairstyle/Peinado/Coiffure_Gandini Club Team
Make-up/Maquillaje/Maquillage_Stefania Pellizzaro
Style/Estilo/Style_Silvia Cicchetti
Photo/Foto/Photo_Paulo Renftle

Hairstyle/Peinado/Coiffure_Charles & Karen Dodds for Cutting Room Creative
Make-up/Maquillaje/Maquillage_Jiada Zenturini
Style/Estilo/Style_Darren Knight

Hairstyle/Peinado/Coiffure_Jean Claude Biguine

Hairstyle/Peinado/Coiffure_Dessange
Photo/Foto/Photo_Nathalie Demontes

Hairstyle/Peinado/Coiffure_Dessange
Photo/Foto/Photo_Nathalie Demontes

Hairstyle/Peinado/Coiffure_*Fellowship Team for F.A.M.E. team***
Make-up/Maquillaje/Maquillage_*Charlotte Foster Brown***
Style/Estilo/Style_*Renwick Blue* *Photo/Foto/Photo_****Andrew O'Toole***

Hairstyle/Peinado/Coiffure_*Jean-Luc Amarin for Camille Albane***
Photo/Foto/Photo_*Nathalie Demontes***

Hairstyle/Peinado/Coiffure_Intercoiffure France
Make-up/Maquillaje/Maquillage_Sebastian
Style/Estilo/Style_Gaélle Bon
Photo/Foto/Photo_Yannick Touzan

Hairstyle/Peinado/Coiffure_Klaus Peter Ochs

Hairstyle/Peinado/Coiffure_Fabien Provost for Franck Provost
Make-up/Maquillaje/Maquillage_Charlotte Willer
Photo/Foto/Photo_Adel Awad

Hairstyle/Peinado/Coiffure_Emiliano Vitale for E Salon
Make-up/Maquillaje/Maquillage_Jenny Eady
Photo/Foto/Photo_Peter Tabor

Hairstyle/Peinado/Coiffure_Rizos Team
Make-up/Maquillaje/Maquillage_Pila Lucas for Rizos
Photo/Foto/Photo_David Arnal

Hairstyle/Peinado/Coiffure_Leonardo Rizzo for Sanrizz

Hairstyle/Peinado/Coiffure_Londa Professional Team (Moscow)
Make-up/Maquillaje/Maquillage_Regina Profiri
Photo/Foto/Photo_Alexander Korobov
Products/Productos/Produits_Londa Professional

Hairstyle/Peinado/Coiffure_Londa Professional Team (Moscow)
Make-up/Maquillaje/Maquillage_Regina Profiri
Photo/Foto/Photo_Alexander Korobov
Products/Productos/Produits_Londa Professional

Hairstyle/Peinado/Coiffure_Yulia Lagnuk
Make-up/Maquillaje/Maquillage_Sergey Ablakov
Photo/Foto/Photo_Alexsey Kasachek

Hairstyle/Peinado/Coiffure_Pavel Vaan
Photo/Foto/Photo_Studio «Koma»

Hairstyle/Peinado/Coiffure_Dessange
Photo/Foto/Photo_Nathalie Demontes

Hair's How
Red/Rojo/Roux

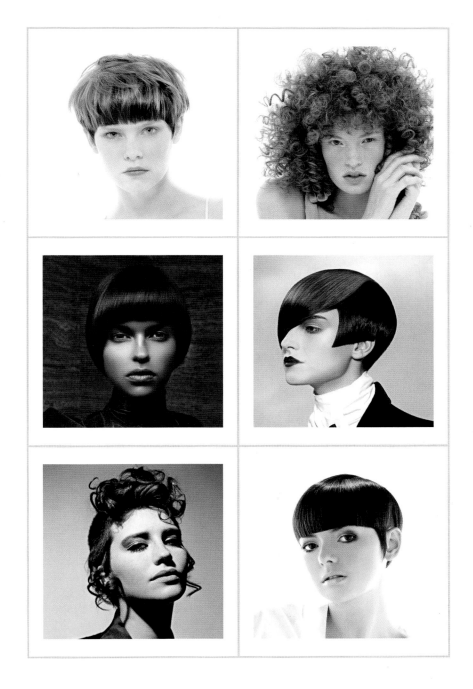

Hairstyle/Peinado/Coiffure_Glenn van Dijke and Keune Studio Team
Make-up/Maquillaje/Maquillage_Dominique Samuelsen
Style/Estilo/Style_Pedro Dias
Photo/Foto/Photo_Hans de Vries

Hairstyle/Peinado/Coiffure_Odile Gilbert for L'Oréal Professionnel
Photo/Foto/Photo_Mark Segal

Hairstyle/Peinado/Coiffure_J7 Team
Photo/Foto/Photo_Vlado Golub

Hairstyle/Peinado/Coiffure_Courtney Treyvaud for Mieka Hairdressing
Make-up/Maquillaje/Maquillage_Benn Jae
Style/Estilo/Style_Jordan Moore
Photo/Foto/Photo_Trevor King

Hairstyle/Peinado/Coiffure_Andrew Barton, Alison Dace, Tracey Gallagher for Saks
Make-up/Maquillaje/Maquillage_Carol Brown
Photo/Foto/Photo_Darren Feist

Hairstyle/Peinado/Coiffure_Suzie McGill for Rainbow Room International
Make-up/Maquillaje/Maquillage_Lee Pearson
Style/Estilo/Style_Bernard Connolly
Photo/Foto/Photo_Christophe Cohen

Hairstyle/Peinado/Coiffure_Keune Team

Hairstyle/Peinado/Coiffure_Paul Mitchell

Hairstyle/Peinado/Coiffure_Gandini International Team
Make-up/Maquillaje/Maquillage_Stefania Pellizzaro
Style/Estilo/Style_Silvia Cicchetti
Photo/Foto/Photo_Paulo Renftle

*Hairstyle/Peinado/Coiffure*_Franck Pérez, Jean Louis David

Hairstyle/Peinado/Coiffure_Paul Mitchell   *Hairstyle/Peinado/Coiffure_Paul Mitchell*

Hairstyle/Peinado/Coiffure_Cathy Monnier and Saint Algue Team
Make-up/Maquillaje/Maquillage_Luc Droguen
Style/Estilo/Style_Alexandra Tesson
Photo/Foto/Photo_Gilles-Marie Zimmermann

***Hairstyle/Peinado/Coiffure**_Colin Greaney for Mahogany*
***Coloring/Teñido/Coloration**_Ciara Fagan & Vivica Davies*
***Style/Estilo/Style**_Amy Abrahams*

***Hairstyle/Peinado/Coiffure**_Richard Thompson, Neil Atkinson,*
Darren Newton, Paul Harewood for Mahogany
***Coloring/Teñido/Coloration**_Ciara Fagan, Vivica Davies*
***Make-up/Maquillaje/Maquillage**_Philippe*

Hairstyle/Peinado/Coiffure_Petra Mechurova
Photo/Foto/Photo_Martin Matejicek

Hairstyle/Peinado/Coiffure_Louise Smith, Toni&Guy
Make-up/Maquillaje/Maquillage_Carolee Hyams
Style/Estilo/Style_Bernard Connolly **Photo/Foto/Photo_Sandro Hyams**

Hairstyle/Peinado/Coiffure_Courtney Treyvaud for Mieka Hairdressing
Make-up/Maquillaje/Maquillage_Benn Jae
Style/Estilo/Style_Jordan Moore **Photo/Foto/Photo_Trevor King**

Hairstyle/Peinado/Coiffure_Michael Barnes for Goldwell
Make-up/Maquillaje/Maquillage_Marco Antonio
Style/Estilo/Style_Chiyono Minagawa
Photo/Foto/Photo_Kyoko Homma

Hairstyle/Peinado/Coiffure_Beverly Rosser
& Beth Sawyer @ Bobbers Hairdressing

Hairstyle/Peinado/Coiffure_Thomas Schug,
Sezai Bingul for Keller The School
Make-up/Maquillaje/Maquillage_Errol Koyu
Photo/Foto/Photo_Vlado Golub

Hairstyle/Peinado/Coiffure_Mark Hayes and Sassoon Creative Team
Make-up/Maquillaje/Maquillage_Daniel Kolaric
Photo/Foto/Photo_Colin Roy

*Hairstyle/Peinado/Coiffure_*Victoria Merushkevich
*Make-up/Maquillaje/Maquillage_*Alexandra Kristoforova

*Hairstyle/Peinado/Coiffure_*Mark Leeson Artistic Team, Mark Leeson Hair,
Body & Mind
*Make-up/Maquillaje/Maquillage_*Kylie O'Toole
*Style/Estilo/Style_*Emma Cotterill *Photo/Foto/Photo_*Andrew O'Toole

Hairstyle/Peinado/Coiffure_Paul Gehring
Make-up/Maquillaje/Maquillage_Christina Marzo, Fabrizio Camponeschi
Photo/Foto/Photo_Carlo Battillocchi

95

Hairstyle/Peinado/Coiffure_Michael Barnes for Goldwell
Make-up/Maquillaje/Maquillage_Marco Antonio
Style/Estilo/Style_Chiyono Minagawa
Photo/Foto/Photo_Kyoko Homma

Hairstyle/Peinado/Coiffure_J7 Team
Photo/Foto/Photo_Vlado Golub

Hairstyle/Peinado/Coiffure_Mark Hayes and Sassoon Creative Team
Make-up/Maquillaje/Maquillage_Daniel Kolaric
Photo/Foto/Photo_Colin Roy

Hairstyle/Peinado/Coiffure_Charles & Karen Dodds for Cutting Room Creative
Make-up/Maquillaje/Maquillage_Jiada Zenturini
Style/Estilo/Style_Darren Knight

Hairstyle/Peinado/Coiffure_Gary Hooker & Michael Young
Make-up/Maquillaje/Maquillage_Kabuki
Photo/Foto/Photo_Malcolm Willison

Hair's How
Creative/Creativo/Créatif

Hairstyle/Peinado/Coiffure_Walkom, Suki Hairdressing for GHD
Make-up/Maquillaje/Maquillage_Aimie Fiebig
Style/Estilo/Style_Michael Azzolini
Photo/Foto/Photo_Steven Chee

Hairstyle/Peinado/Coiffure_Walkom, Suki Hairdressing for GHD
Make-up/Maquillaje/Maquillage_Aimie Fiebig
Style/Estilo/Style_Michael Azzolini
Photo/Foto/Photo_Steven Chee

***Hairstyle/Peinado/Coiffure_**Massimo Di Stefano, Lesley Lawson for Schwarzkopf Professional*
***Make-up/Maquillaje/Maquillage_**Alexsandra Byrne*
***Style/Estilo/Style_**Lucy Manning*
***Photo/Foto/Photo_**Simon Emmett*

Hairstyle/Peinado/Coiffure_Walkom, Suki Hairdressing for GHD
Make-up/Maquillaje/Maquillage_Aimie Fiebig
Style/Estilo/Style_Michael Azzolini
Photo/Foto/Photo_Steven Chee

Hairstyle/Peinado/Coiffure_Michal Zapomel
Make-up/Maquillaje/Maquillage_Ivana Torkaska
Style/Estilo/Style_Boris Hanecka

Hairstyle/Peinado/Coiffure_Michal Zapomel
Make-up/Maquillaje/Maquillage_Ivana Torkaska
Style/Estilo/Style_Boris Hanecka

Hairstyle/Peinado/Coiffure_Goldwell Creative Team

Hairstyle/Peinado/Coiffure_Louise Smith, Toni&Guy
Make-up/Maquillaje/Maquillage_Carolee Hyams
Style/Estilo/Style_Bernard Connolly
Photo/Foto/Photo_Sandro Hyams

Hairstyle/Peinado/Coiffure_Karine Jackson
Make-up/Maquillaje/Maquillage_Margaret Aston
Photo/Foto/Photo_Andrew O'Toole

Hairstyle/Peinado/Coiffure_Thomas Schug, Sezai Bingul for Keller The School
Make-up/Maquillaje/Maquillage_Errol Koyu
Photo/Foto/Photo_Vlado Golub

Hairstyle/Peinado/Coiffure_J7 Creative Team
Photo/Foto/Photo_Vlado Golub

***Hairstyle/Peinado/Coiffure**_Mark Hayes for Sassoon Creative Team*
***Make-up/Maquillaje/Maquillage**_Candice Winkelpleck*
***Style/Estilo/Style**_Tabitha Owen **Photo/Foto/Photo**_Luke Duval*

***Hairstyle/Peinado/Coiffure**_Mark Hayes for Sassoon Creative Team*
***Make-up/Maquillaje/Maquillage**_Candice Winkelpleck*
***Style/Estilo/Style**_Tabitha Owen **Photo/Foto/Photo**_Luke Duval*

Hairstyle/Peinado/Coiffure_Tracey Hughes, Vanessa Plesnicar for Mieka Hairdressing
Make-up/Maquillaje/Maquillage_Sina Velke
Style/Estilo/Style_Cassandra Scott-Finn
Photo/Foto/Photo_Marija Ikovic

Hairstyle/Peinado/Coiffure_Thomas Schug,
Sezai Bingul for Keller The School
Make-up/Maquillaje/Maquillage_Errol Koyu **Photo**/Foto/Photo_*Vlado Golub*

Hairstyle/Peinado/Coiffure_Thomas Schug,
Sezai Bingul for Keller The School
Make-up/Maquillaje/Maquillage_Errol Koyu **Photo**/Foto/Photo_*Vlado Golub*

Hairstyle/Peinado/Coiffure_Thomas Schug,
Sezai Bingul for Keller The School
Make-up/Maquillaje/Maquillage_Errol Koyu
Photo/Foto/Photo_Vlado Golub

Hairstyle/Peinado/Coiffure_Goldwell Creative Team

Hairstyle/Peinado/Coiffure_Tracey Hughes for Mieka Hairdressing
Make-up/Maquillaje/Maquillage_Benn Jae
Photo/Foto/Photo_Marija Ikovic

Volume 9 / Volumen 9 / Volume 9

COLOR / TEÑIDO / COULEUR

Published by / Publicado por / Publié par

HAIR'S HOW
5645 Coral Ridge Drive # 131
Coral Springs, FL 33076, USA
Ph. 1-954-323-8590, Fax 1-951-344-2240
e-mail: publisher@hairshow.us

Distributed by / Distribuido por / Distribué par

HAIR'S HOW
5645 Coral Ridge Drive # 131
Coral Springs, FL 33076, USA
Ph. 1-954-323-8590, Fax 1-951-344-2240
www.hairshow.us, e-mail: sales@hairshow.us

HAIR'S HOW Vol. 9: Color
HAIR'S HOW Vol. 9: Teñido
HAIR'S HOW Vol. 9: Couleur

ISBN 978-0-9822037-1-2

Printed in EU / Impreso en EU / Imprimé en Europe

First edition / Primera edición / Première édition